I LOVE CAMP!

TODD PARR

061928.3K2/B336/A3   Printed in China

When summer comes, some kids like to swim, some enjoy hikes or have picnics with friends, and others read books or play outside a lot. I get to do all of these great things and more, all in one place! That's why I LOVE CAMP.

When I go to camp fun things happen like...

Doing arts and crafts.

Taking care of the garden.

Singing Hebrew songs around the campfire.

Birds sing, frogs ribbit,

squirrels scoot, grasshoppers hop.

I spend time with cool camp counselors from different places.

And make new friends.

SHALOM CHAVERIM

When I go to camp exciting things happen like...

Rock climbing.

Canoeing.

Israeli dancing.

Gathering for meals.

Swimming.

Playing all kinds of sports.

gaga pit

And having a spectacular talent show.

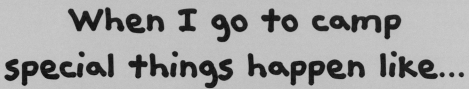

When I go to camp
special things happen like...

Celebrating Shabbat.

Noshing on tasty treats.

when you go to Jewish summer camp, you will make a lot of new friends, learn new things, eat good food and sing cool songs. You will have so much fun you won't want to leave. ♥ Love, Todd

Using This Book at Home

Each page of **I Love Camp!** pictures an animal. Challenge your little ones to find the animals, count and/or name them. They might also count trees, children wearing hats, or the pages showing water.

This book shows camp as a fabulous place with happy, busy children. Invite your children to count the smiling faces in the book. There are a lot!

Look for Jewish objects throughout the book. Talk about where you might have noticed these objects, during which Jewish holiday they are commonly seen, and how they are used.

Discuss with your children any activities pictured in the book in which your family has taken part or that you would enjoy.

Israeli dancing is popular at many Jewish summer camps. Locate some lively Israeli music at your local library, music store, or online and, as a family, get up and dance together!

Explore Jewish camps online. Ask your children to point out any photos of children doing activities similar to those they noticed in this book.

The cover of **I Love Camp!** shows children on a bus. With cardboard boxes, paint, markers, etc., create a camp bus. While "sitting on the bus," sing favorite songs — "The People on the Bus," for example — or play travel games, such as I Spy.

Is there a Jewish summer camp in your area? If so, take a family drive to check it out. If camp is in session, arrange in advance for a tour.

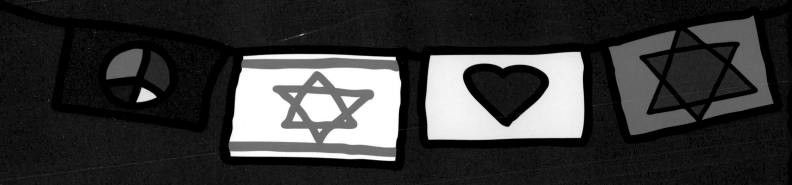

Glossary of Terms

GAGA: an Israeli version of dodge ball. "Gaga" is Hebrew, meaning "hit, hit." The game is often played in an enclosed area known as a "gaga pit."

HAVDALAH: a short ceremony on Saturday evening marking the end of the Jewish Sabbath and the beginning of a new week. "Havdalah" is Hebrew, meaning "separation."

HINEI MA TOV: the title of a well-known Jewish song. The lyrics come from Psalm 133 and translate from Hebrew: "How pleasant it is when people live together in harmony."

MAZEL TOV: a phrase used to offer congratulations. The phrase is a combination of the Yiddish mazel ("luck" or "fortune") and the Hebrew tov ("good.")

NOSH: from the Yiddish, meaning "eat a snack."

OMANOOT: the Hebrew word for "art."

SHABBAT: the Jewish Sabbath, the weekly day of rest that begins on Friday evening and ends when three stars are visible in the Saturday night sky.

SHALOM: a Hebrew word with three distinct meanings – "hello," "goodbye," and "peace."

SHALOM CHAVERIM: a Hebrew phrase meaning "Hello, friends." It is also the title of a popular Hebrew song.

TEVA: the Hebrew word for "nature."